Gracie

WITH GIFTS FROM ABOVE

GRACIE WITH GIFTS FROM ABOVE

Copyright © 1987 Anne FitzGerald

ISBN 0-85009-128-4 (Australia 1-86248-026-X)

Printed in Italy.
Worldwide co-edition organised and produced by Angus Hudson Ltd, London.

WORD PUBLISHING
Word (UK) Ltd
England

Word Books Australia, Sunday School Centre Wholesale South Africa, Alby Commercial Enterprises Pte Ltd Singapore, Concorde Distributors Ltd New Zealand, Cross (HK) Company Hong Kong, Eunsung Corp Korea, Praise Inc Philippines.

♡

Gracie

KNOWS EVERY GOOD
AND PERFECT GIFT COMES
FROM THE FATHER ABOVE.~~~

HERE'S A FEW VERY SPECIAL GIFTS
JUST FOR YOU!

LOVE

I COR. 13:13

OF THESE THREE
FAITH, HOPE AND LOVE
LOVE IS THE GREATEST ——

THE BIGGEST GIFT OF ALL !

JOY

PROVERBS 17:22

A MERRY HEART
DOES GOOD LIKE
MEDICINE. —.

WHEN YOU CAN'T THINK
OR PRAY ... TRY A SONG OF PRAISE

PEACE

JOHN 14:27

MY PEACE I GIVE
... NOT AS THE
WORLD GIVES

YOU'LL KNOW THE DIFFERENCE
... HIS IS LASTING

WISDOM

JAMES 1:5

IF ANYONE NEEDS WISDOM
LET HIM ASK GOD AND HE
WILL GIVE IT TO HIM

... ALL YOU HAVE TO DO
IS ASK !

STRENGTH

PHIL. 4:13

I CAN DO EVERYTHING
THROUGH CHRIST WHO
GIVES ME STRENGTH

REMEMBER WHEN YOU CAN'T
··· HE CAN

FAITH

ROMANS 10:17

FAITH COMES BY
HEARING THE WORD
OF GOD

...FEED YOUR FAITH
DAILY

FREEDOM

John 8:36

IF THE SON SETS YOU FREE
YOU ARE FREE
INDEED

YOU HAVE BEEN SET FREE
... TAKE FLIGHT!

TRUST

2 TIM. 1:12

HE WILL TAKE CARE
OF WHAT YOU'VE
COMMITTED TO HIM

... A PERFECT PLACE
FOR ALL YOUR PROBLEMS

REST

MATT. 11:28

COME TO ME ALL THAT
LABOUR AND ARE HEAVY
LADEN
     ... AND I WILL GIVE
       YOU REST~~~.

SLOW DOWN
    ... AND TAKE IT!

LIGHT

PSALM 119: 105
THY WORD IS A LAMP
TO MY FEET AND A LIGHT
TO MY PATH

NO NEED TO STUMBLE
        AROUND IN THE DARK

CONFIDENCE

2 TIM. 1:7

FOR GOD HAS NOT GIVEN
US A SPIRIT OF TIMIDITY
BUT OF POWER AND
OF LOVE AND A SOUND
                    MIND

... GO FOR IT!

CONTENTMENT

PSALM 23:1

FOR THE LORD
IS MY SHEPHERD
I HAVE EVERYTHING.
    YES,— I HAVE EVERYTHING
       I NEED !

... AND HE KNOWS BEST
JUST WHAT YOU NEED

WONDERFUL GIFTS
FROM ABOVE !

HE
SENT THEM
NOW
You CAN
RECEIVE
THEM